Chocolate Chuckles

by **Pam Harvey**

illustrated by **Janine Dawson**

The Characters

Sally

Mum

Grandpa and Grandma

The Setting

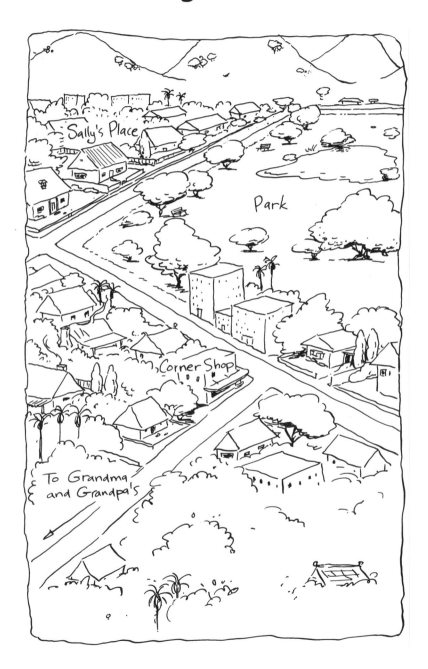

CONTENTS

I say 'luckily for me' because Mum couldn't see the empty milk carton I'd just been drinking from.

"They'll be here any minute. And he'll want a cup of tea," said Mum.

'He' was Grandpa, the birthday boy, who drank twenty cups of tea a day. He used the same tea bag which he lugged around all day in a little green tin in his pocket. Disgusting!

Except one fairy cake and one crisp —
but they didn't really count.

Something was bugging me and I had to nibble to help me think. Something was missing from the party food — and I didn't mean the fairy cake and the crisp.

Then it came to me — there were no chocolate crispie cakes!

"What's a party without chocolate crispie cakes?" I thought. I stood up. Things were desperate. There were thirteen minutes left before Mum came back.

CHAPTER 2

Making Chocolate Crispie Cakes

I bolted across to the pantry and pulled the door open.

Have you ever made chocolate crispie cakes? You have? Well, I hadn't. I'd eaten one million, seven hundred and sixty-five thousand, three hundred and twenty-one in my lifetime, so you'd think I'd know what was in them.

I thought very hard. Mum had made
chocolate crispie cakes for every one
of my birthdays. I could picture her
mixing bowl in my head. Hmmm.

In it there were rice bubbles, some chocolate, a sort of white stuff and a sort of kitchen glue to stick it all together.

The rice bubbles were easy to find because Mum kept them in a see-through plastic container. I poured a heap into the bowl. Cocoa powder would do as the chocolate stuff — half a tin went in. But the white stuff was a bit trickier.

Pantries are full of white stuff — ever noticed? Whole shelves of containers with nothing written on them, and the contents all look like talcum powder.

My best guess for the mystery white stuff was sugar, but I ate some and it was too crunchy. Chocolate crispie cakes don't feel gritty when you chomp into them. I knew it wasn't flour as then they wouldn't be chocolate crispie cakes, they'd be chocolate cakes.

At last, I found a packet of white stuff
that wasn't gritty and wasn't floury. The
label said bicarbonate of soda. That didn't
help, but I was nearly out of time.

I poured the whole box in. Then, to stick it all together, I gollumped in some olive oil.

Mix, mix, mix.

It looked perfect: brown, gooey and bubbly. It was just a matter of chucking lumps into those paper cake cases and BINGO! Chocolate crispie cakes.

The Party

I put a plate full of chocolate crispie cakes with the rest of the party food on the table.

Just then, I heard Mum pull up in the drive. Another car pulled up straight behind her, so I had time to wash the mixing bowl.

Bits of chocolate crispie cake clung to my fingers and I licked them off.

There was something strange about the taste. Something quite different! I figured that was because they weren't set.

The taste grew stronger in my mouth and was really odd. I was downing a glass of water when Grandpa, Grandma, Uncle Bill and Aunty Jean burst through the door in one long flow.

"I'm not going to do it, Mabel," Grandpa was saying. He looked really grumpy and he was shaking his head.

"My teeth are staying in my head until
I die." He waggled them with his tongue.
They were the most disgusting set of
false teeth you've ever seen.

"They're so worn!" said Grandma.

"It would be much easier to chew with new ones," said Mum.

"Wouldn't get me near a dentist," said
Uncle Bill.

"I once knew a man who was ninety-seven
and still had his own teeth," said Aunty
Jean.

"Happy Birthday, Grandpa," I said.

Grandpa grunted and gave me a pat on the shoulder.

"If you can get my teeth out of my head then I'll go and get new ones. But they're in and they're staying in," said Grandpa finally.

Grandpa Loves Chocolate Crispie Cakes

Grandpa rubbed his hands together as he looked around at the party food. "This looks like a great spread. Make this for me, Love?"

"Parts of it," I said with a quick look at Mum. "I opened the jar of pickled onions for you."

"My favourites!" said Grandpa, and picked up the bowl. He started eating the onions as if they were bits of popcorn. Old people have the weirdest tastes!

"Dad!" said Mum. "The party doesn't start until the others get here."

"**My** party," said Grandpa with his mouth full of onions. "**My** food." He stalked around the table looking for other things.

"Aha!" he said. "Chocolate crispie cakes."

"Chocolate crispie cakes?" said Mum.
"I didn't make chocolate crispie cakes."

I was feeling pretty proud of myself.
It was probably the first time I'd ever
done anything useful in the kitchen.

"I made them, Grandpa," I said, holding
up the plate for him. "They're not set
yet, so you'll have to hold onto them
carefully."

Grandpa put the now empty onion bowl down, and rubbed his hands together again.

"After pickled onions," he said, "there's nothing I like better than chocolate crispie cakes."

He scooped two up, one in each hand, and jammed them into his mouth one after the other.

At first I thought that the strange expression on his face was because his false teeth weren't working properly. Then I realised that his teeth wouldn't make his eyes bulge.

There was a rumbling sound coming from
him. It sounded like a really deep chuckle.

Suddenly Grandpa's cheeks puffed up and out of his mouth came a flood of white froth.

"What's happening?" screamed Aunty Jean.

"He's having a fit!" said Uncle Bill.

"His insides are coming out!" yelled
Grandma.

"What did you put in those chocolate crispie cakes?" screeched Mum.

Grandpa's cheeks puffed and sank, puffed and sank and a great tide of rice bubble flecked foam poured out of his mouth. With it came two pink and yellow things that looked a lot like broken pottery.

Then I realised what they were — Grandpa's teeth!

CHAPTER 5

Will Grandpa Be OK?

"Is this what you used?" Mum said, waving the empty box of bicarbonate of soda at me.

"Isn't that what you put in chocolate crispie cakes?" I asked. "I've seen you put white stuff in."

"Icing sugar! Icing sugar, not bicarbonate of soda!" Mum dropped the packet on the floor and covered her face with her hands.

I was really worried. She seemed so upset. What had I done to Grandpa? Does bicarbonate of soda hurt you?

Mum looked up. She wasn't crying at all, she was laughing! Laughing so much her mouth was wide open and I could see all her fillings.

"The bicarbonate of soda's reacted with the pickled onions," she said, as she tried to stop laughing.

I remembered a science experiment at
school. Mix vinegar and bicarbonate of
soda and vlumvlumvlum — white froth.
It's how you make pretend volcanoes.

I looked at Grandpa. The stuff coming
out of his mouth was just the same as
the stuff we'd made at school. Only we'd
put red colouring in our volcano so it
looked more like hot lava. Grandpa's froth
just looked like lots of toothpaste spit.

Except that his teeth had come out with it.

Grandma noticed that, too.

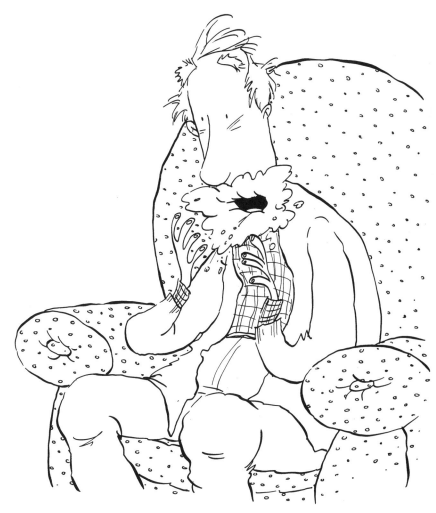

She moved faster than I'd ever seen her move. Darting forward she grabbed Grandpa's teeth and shoved them into her pocket.

"Gibembag," said Grandpa.

"No." Grandma patted her pocket. "They're out and they stay out until you get new ones."

Grandma might only be little, but you can't argue with someone who's got your teeth! Especially if you're spitting suds everywhere and no one can understand you.

Grandpa sighed, spraying everyone with great gobs of white froth.

In the end, Grandpa had a great eightieth birthday. He sat on a chair in the middle of the room eating mashed birthday cake all afternoon.

He said to me, (it took me half an hour to understand) that the indigestion he'd felt for three years had suddenly gone. It must have been the dose of bicarbonate of soda.

I didn't know what he meant. Maybe I'll find out in a month or two. Mum's enrolled me in a cooking course. She said it would teach me the difference between all the white stuff in the pantry.

As long as we don't have to eat the things we make!

GLOSSARY

bicarbonate of soda
powder used to help things
rise in cooking

bulge
a part that sticks out

desperate
having no hope

enrolled
joined a class

gritty
feels like it has bits of sand in it

indigestion
a burning feeling
in your tummy

lifetime
the length of time you are alive

nibble
to eat little bits of

pantry
a cupboard where
food is kept

talcum powder
a powder you put
on after bathing

waggled
to move with short,
quick movements

Pam Harvey

What is your favourite thing?

> I have a silver bracelet that is made out of two spoons welded together. I wear that bracelet everywhere and it's left a dent in my arm.

What do you like about yourself?

> I like the way I smile a lot, even when things aren't very funny.

Why did the cow jump over the moon?

> Because she had very long legs with lots of stringy ligaments in them like kangaroos have. Does this make her a cowaroo?

What is your best midnight snack?

> At midnight, the house is very quiet so I have to eat something that doesn't crunch or I'd wake everyone. I eat dried quince and sultanas.

Janine Dawson

What is your favourite thing?

> Me and Rosie cracking up over something that the cats did (especially when one gets accidentally frightened and springs straight up in the air!)

What do you like about yourself?

> The fact that I love to draw.

Why did the cow jump over the moon?

> Methane. (I've almost managed it myself at times.)

What is your best midnight snack?

> Toast and honey.